AMAZING
WOMAN

JODERE

GROUP

SAN DIEGO, CALIFORNIA

AMAZING
WOMAN

A Celebration of the Love We Share

A Personal Journey

MARSH ENGLE

Copyright © 2002 by Marsh Engle

Published by Jodere Group, Inc.
P.O. Box 910147, San Diego, CA 92191-0147
(800) 569-1002 • www.jodere.com

Cover design by Steven Guddat
Book design by Charles McStravick

CIP data available from the Library of Congress

ISBN 1-58872-031-4

04 03 02 01   4 3 2 1
1st printing, February 2002

Printed in Canada

Amazing Wo

About This Journal

Amazing Woman: A Celebration of the Love We Share has been created to help you express—through guided journal entries—the love and inspiration you feel for an amazing woman in your life.

Through a gathering of questions, you will recapture the colossal journey of memories and experiences. The words on each page are designed to encourage the spilling forward of your thoughts and feelings. Express freely and have fun with these pages. It is here that you will record the essence of adventure and shared moments. Each page will become a personal expression of the appreciation you feel for an amazing woman.

Celebrate her life of inspiration!

Let's begin now . . .

The Amazing Woman

She's found in
an outreached hand, a word of encouragement,
an expression of truth, an honest perspective,
an interested listener, an inner strength,
a single voice of love and inspiration.

You are an amazing woman!

A Celebration of You!

To:

From:

Date:

Occasion:

Special Thoughts

Personal message about this book:

Amazing Wo...

aying Woman

Remembering Back in Time

The moment we met:

A Perfect Day

I knew we really liked each other when:

Favorites

Words and Sayings:

My favorite memory of the time we spent together is:

The place I loved visiting the most with you is:

I love to hear the story you tell about:

My favorite picture of you:

My favorite picture of us:

Amazing Wo

Amazing Woman

Glimmer

A dazzling journey
leading to a life
awakened in love!

Laughter

It always makes me laugh when I think of the time you:

Remember how much fun we had when we:

Love

Your expression of love touches my life by:

Enthusiasm

Your love of life inspires me to:

Encouragement

You encourage me to become the mirror of your . . .

. . . greatest strength:

. . . spoken words of truth:

. . . expression of kindness:

. . . love and patience:

Wisdom

Perfectly perfect, the excursion guiding me to now
Merely an amazing expedition to awaken desire
Simply so that I could remember
Simply so that I could feel
How perfectly perfect life is
being as I am.
Love

Forgiveness

Your ability to forgive helped me to recognize:

Amazing Wo

Amazing Woman

Words

Words you have said helped me to recognize:

Your words of love have helped me to believe:

Trust

I knew I could trust you when:

I can always count on you because:

Honesty

Your words of honesty have helped me discover:

Listening

Thank you for listening when:

Imagination

Become free to dance boldly
love immensely
and give with abandon!

Adventure

Your sense of adventure inspires me to try new things!

I admire the way you dare to:

I respect that you took a risk and faced the unknown to:

Dreams

You inspire my dreams of:

Thank you for sharing your dream with me about:

Remember the dream we shared together about:

Passions

You inspired me to discover my passion for . . .

. . . a sport, hobby or fun activity:

. . . a favorite book, movie, play or music:

Courage

I admire your courage to . . .

. . . try new things like:

. . . offer an honest opinion about:

. . . face a difficult choice:

. . . allow your emotions to be expressed:

You inspired me to discover the courage to:

Just for Fun!

Five words that I think of when I think of you:

1.

2.

3.

4.

5.

. . . I smile when I think of:

The color that most reminds me of you is . . .

. . . Ocean Blue

When you:

. . . Sunshine Yellow

When you:

. . . Fire Red

When you:

. . . Bubblegum Pink

When you:

. . . Lily White

When you:

. . . Color:

When you:

. . . Color:

When you:

Reminders of You!

Favorite Books:

Amazing Wo...

W...
...azing Woman

Favorite Songs:

Special Thoughts of You

Zest is the secret of all beauty.
There is no beauty that is attractive without zest.

Christian Dior

To learn more about Amazing Women visit
www.AmazingWomen.org

We hope you enjoyed this Jodere Group book.
If you would like additional information
about Jodere Group, Inc., please contact:

JODERE
GROUP

P.O. Box 910147
San Diego, CA 92191-0147
(800) 569-1002
www.jodere.com